Disney Learning

Disney PRINCESS

READING COMPREHENSION

Bendon Publishing International, Inc.
Ashland, OH 44805
www.bendonpub.com

©2007 Disney Enterprises, Inc.

Sleeping Beauty

Long ago in a kingdom far away, a princess was born to a happy king and queen. Three good fairies were invited to bless the child. Flora gave Aurora the gift of beauty. Fauna gave her the gift of song.

Then the evil sorceress Maleficent appeared. She was very angry that she was not invited.

"Oh, it is a shame that you are not happy to see me," she said. "There was no invitation. I thought that was a mistake. Well, nevermind, I have a gift for the child. She will grow in beauty and grace, but on her sixteenth birthday she will prick her finger on a spinning wheel and die."

After Maleficent left, the third good fairy gave Aurora her gift. Merryweather told King Stefan and the Queen she could not take away Maleficent's curse. She could only change it. Aurora would prick her finger, but she would not die. Instead, she would fall into a deep sleep only to be awakened by True Love's Kiss.

The fairies said Aurora could live with them in the woods and be safe. After her sixteenth birthday she would come home.

When that day finally came, the fairies sent Aurora into the woods to pick some berries so they could surprise her with a party. As Aurora walked along, she sang. A handsome young man was riding through the forest and heard her.

They talked, and liked each other very much. Aurora asked him to come to the house that night.

What did you read?

Directions: Now that you have read the first part of the story, answer the questions below.

1. What name did the king and queen give to their new child?

_____

2. How many good fairies were invited to bless the child?

_____

3. Aurora would fall into a deep sleep only to be awakened by what?

_____

4. Where did Aurora live with the fairies to be safe?

_____

Match the fairies

Directions: Each good fairy gave Aurora a gift. Draw a line from the name of each fairy to the gift she gave Aurora.

Fauna	The gift of beauty
Flora	To be awoken by True Love's Kiss
Merryweather	The gift of song

When Aurora returned, the fairies told her the best part of her birthday surprise. It was time for her to go and live in the castle. But Aurora was not happy. She told them about the young man she met in the woods. She said he was coming back to see her.

The good fairies told her she should not fall in love with him. She was a princess and she had to marry a prince. Her real home was the castle.

Maleficent was waiting at the castle. It did not take long for the princess to fall under her spell. Aurora climbed up the dark tower steps. In the tower room was a spinning wheel. She reached out to touch it. She could not stop herself. Maleficent appeared. She had won.

The fairies hurried to find Aurora, but they were too late. She had fallen into a deep sleep. Only True Love's Kiss could awaken her. Then, the fairies remembered the young man Aurora had met in the woods. They were sure Aurora loved him. Casting a spell, the good fairies had everyone sleep until they found Aurora's true love.

Before falling asleep, the prince's father said his son was in love with a girl he had met. Remembering what Aurora said, the fairies understood. Prince Phillip was Aurora's true love! Flora, Fauna, and Merryweather hurried out to look for the prince. They found him prisoner in Maleficent's castle and set him free, giving him the Shield of Virtue and the Sword of Truth.

© Disney

Maleficent turned herself into a dragon and charged toward the prince. The dragon forced the prince out on the edge of a cliff. He had nowhere to go, but he could not fall. He had to save Aurora. He threw his enchanted sword into the dragon's heart. The dragon roared in pain.

Prince Phillip raced back to the castle and found Aurora. He bent down and kissed her. She woke up, and so did everyone else.

That night there was a ball. Aurora and the prince danced for a long time. The two fathers watched for a while. Then they started to plan a royal wedding.

What did you read?

Directions: Now that you have read the second part of the story, answer the questions below.

1. What was the birthday surprise that the fairies had for Aurora?

_____

2. Why couldn't Aurora fall in love with the young man?

_____

3. When Aurora reached the tower room, what did she find?

_____

4. What kind of creature did Maleficent turn herself into?

_____

Cinderella

Once there was a kind and gentle girl named Cinderella. Everyone loved her, even the mice in the hall and the birds in the garden.

Cinderella's stepmother pretended to be kind, but she was lazy and mean. Her stepsisters were mean and lazy, too. Poor Cinderella had to do all of the cooking, sewing, and cleaning.

One day, Cinderella was sweeping. She heard a knock on the door.

"Open in the name of the King!" someone called.

She hurried to the door. It was a messenger. He gave her a big white envelope.

It said that every maiden in the kingdom was invited to a ball.

The mean Stepmother said Cinderella could go IF she finished her work. "Oh, and of course you will need a ball gown," she added. She thought Cinderella would not be able to find one.

Cinderella did find a gown. It had been her mother's. It was pretty, but old. While Cinderella was finishing her work, the birds and the mice fixed the dress using sashes and ribbons the stepsisters had thrown away.

When her stepsisters saw Cinderella's gown, they were angry. They tore off the sashes. The gown was ruined.

What did you read?

Directions: Now that you have read the first part of the story, answer the questions below.

1. Cinderella's stepmother was not kind. What two words describe her?

   _____

2. When Cinderella was sweeping, what did she hear?

   _____

3. What did the messenger bring to her door?

   _____

4. Whose gown did the birds and mice fix for Cinderella?

   _____

Kind words

Directions: Look at these words from the first part of the story. Circle only the words that describe Cinderella's stepmother or stepsisters.

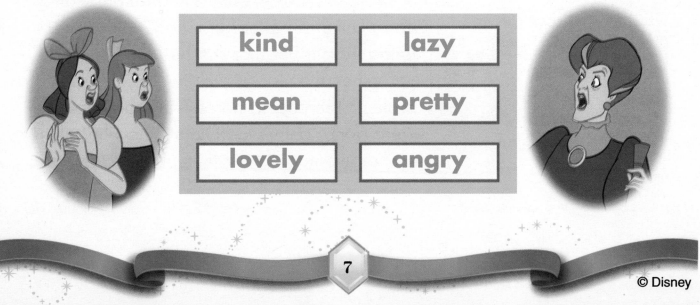

kind	lazy
mean	pretty
lovely	angry

Cinderella sat down in the garden and cried. Her Fairy Godmother came to help. She waved her wand. A pumpkin became a fine coach. Cinderella's mice friends became four white horses.

Next, the Fairy Godmother changed Cinderella's torn dress into a ball gown. Cinderella's old shoes became sparkling glass slippers. The Fairy Godmother said the spell would end at the last stroke of twelve. Everything would change back into what it had

been before. She told Cinderella she had to be back before midnight.

The Prince did not like any of the girls he met at the ball. Then he saw Cinderella. He walked right by the stepsisters, who were bowing to him.

He asked Cinderella to dance. She said yes.

They danced and danced. Cinderella was very happy. Then she heard the clock chime. It was the first stroke of midnight! "I must go," she said.

She ran out the door and down the steps. One of her glass slippers fell off. The Prince and the Grand Duke ran after her. The Grand Duke found the slipper that she had left behind.

When the clock struck twelve, the spell was broken. The coach, horses, and ball gown were gone, but Cinderella still had her glass slipper. She also had happy memories of the ball.

The Prince did not know Cinderella's name. The slipper she had lost was his only clue. He promised to marry the girl whose foot fit the shoe.

When the Grand Duke came to the house, the stepsisters were excited. Each of them tried on the slipper, but it did not fit. It was too small.

The wicked Stepmother had locked Cinderella up in her room, but she got out. She came to the top of the stairs. She asked to try on the slipper.

"Yes, come down. Every maiden must try on the slipper," the Grand Duke said.

Cinderella slipped her foot into the glass slipper. It fit perfectly. She had always known it would.

The mean Stepmother and her daughters were very angry. Cinderella and the Grand Duke went to the palace together. The Prince was happy to see Cinderella again. Soon after, they were married.

What did you read?

Directions: Now that you have read the second part of the story, answer the questions below.

1. What did the Fairy Godmother turn the pumpkin and the mice into?

_____

2. What time did the Fairy Godmother say the spell would end?

_____

3. Who ran after Cinderella after she left? What did they find?

_____

Beauty and the Beast

Once there was a pretty girl named Belle. She loved to read and dream. A hunter named Gaston wanted to marry her, but she did not like him. She dreamed of someday meeting a handsome prince.

Belle's father was an inventor. He was always trying to make things.

One day her father showed Belle a wonderful new invention.

"I will take it to the fair tomorrow," he said.

"I know you will win first prize," Belle said.

Just then there was a big BOOM. It came from the invention.

"It just needs a little more work," her father said.

Her father worked hard to fix his invention. The next day it was ready, so he started off for the fair. He got lost in the woods. There were wild animals. The horse was afraid of them. It threw the old man off of its back. Then it ran away with the cart.

Belle found the horse and cart. Her father was not with them.

"You must take me to Papa," she said to the horse.

She climbed up on its back. Thick fog filled the woods, making it hard to see. Wild animals growled all around, but she rode on. At last she saw a castle.

Belle went into the castle. Her father was locked up.

"Oh, Papa!" Belle said. She gave him a big hug.

What did you read?

Directions: Now that you have read the first part of the story, answer the questions below.

1. Name two things that Belle loved to do.

_____

2. Where was Belle's father taking his new invention?

_____

3. Where did Belle find her father locked up?

_____

Belle and Papa

Directions: Look at these words from the first part of the story. Draw lines from either Belle or Papa to the words that go with each person best.

lost	Belle	inventor
reader		old
dreamer	Papa	pretty

An ugly Beast in a cape appeared. "I found this man in my castle," the Beast said. "Now he is my prisoner."

"Please let him go. I will stay in his place," Belle said.

The Beast made Belle promise to stay with him forever. After letting her father go, the Beast led Belle to her room.

After the Beast left, Belle was amazed to find out that his teapot, clock, and cup could talk. They told her they used to be servants at the castle. All of them had been put under a spell. Belle was glad to have friends, but she was still sad.

Meanwhile, Belle's father ran back to town. He told everyone about the Beast. But nobody believed him. So Belle's father set out to rescue her himself. Gaston wanted to rescue Belle. If he saved her, she would have to marry him.

Over time Belle learned that the Beast was not really mean. He was gentle and sweet. One night she danced with him. Then Belle told the Beast that she missed her father. She had to go home. The Beast did not stop her.

Back at home, Belle took care of her father. Gaston came to visit them. He asked Belle to marry him. She said no. Gaston got angry. He could tell that Belle's heart belonged to the Beast. He convinced the villagers that the Beast was dangerous.

What did you read?

Directions: Now that you have read the middle part of the story, answer the questions below.

1. After letting her father go, where did the Beast take Belle?

_____

2. What did the teapot, clock and cup used to be?

_____

3. Over time, Belle found that the Beast was not mean. What two words describe what Belle thought of him as they danced?

_____

True or False?

Directions: Read each statement and circle the correct answer.

1. The Beast found Papa in his castle.   True   False

2. The Beast used to be a servant.   True   False

3. Gaston asked Belle to marry him.   True   False

4. The villagers thought the Beast was kind.   True   False

Belle and her father rode through the woods as fast as they could. Belle did not want anyone to get hurt. When they got to the castle, Belle saw Gaston and the Beast. They were out on a high balcony. Gaston was raising his bow. He shot the Beast with an arrow.

Belle started crying. She ran up the stairs.

The Beast saw Belle standing there. He picked Gaston up by the neck.

"Let me go!" said Gaston.

The Beast put Gaston down and told him to go.

Gaston did not go. He stabbed the Beast in the back. The Beast roared in pain. Gaston stepped back. He slipped and fell off the balcony.

The Beast lay in Belle's arms. He was dying. "You came back," he said. "I got to see you once more."

"No! Do not die," said Belle. "I love you."

Then something strange and wonderful happened.

In his place stood a handsome prince. The Beast had been a prince all the time, but he was under a spell. When he loved Belle and she loved him, the spell was broken. The Beast became a prince again and all the enchanted things in the castle turned back into servants.

Belle and the Prince danced together.

"I am so happy," said the Prince.

© Disney

What did you read?

Directions: Now that you have read the end of the story, answer the questions below.

1. Who did Belle see on the balcony?

    _____

2. What was broken when Belle told the Beast she loved him?

    _____

3. When the spell was broken, what did the Beast turn into?

    _____

Belle or Beast

Directions: Look at these words in the list below. Put an **X** across any of the words that are **NOT** in the last part of the story.

roared	disliked
slipped	handsome
happy	enchanted
lost	hurt
car	ugly

Snow White and the Seven Dwarfs

There once was a princess named Snow White. She lived in a palace with her mean stepmother, the Queen. The Queen was proud to be the most beautiful woman in the kingdom. Every day she stood in front of a Magic Mirror.

"Magic Mirror on the wall, who is the fairest one of all?" she asked. The Mirror always gave the same answer, "You are."

Then one day it gave a different answer. It said Snow White was the most beautiful.

The Queen was very angry. She called her Huntsman. She held out a box to him.

"You must take Snow White into the forest and do away with her. Put her heart in this box and bring it back to me," she said.

The Huntsman told Snow White that the Queen wanted her to pick some wildflowers for the table. The princess sang as she went into the woods with him. She ran here and there to pick flowers. Even if it meant giving up his own life, the Huntsman realized that he could not hurt her.

Kneeling down before her he said, "Princess, the Queen is jealous of your beauty. She wanted me to kill you. You must run away. You must never come back."

What did you read?

Directions: Now that you have read the first part of the story, answer the questions below.

1. Who lived in the palace with Snow White?

_____

2. The Queen was proud to be beautiful. What did she stand in front of everyday?

_____

3. Where did the Queen want the Huntsman to take Snow White?

_____

4. The Huntsman did not kill Snow White. What did he tell her to do?

_____

Who said what?

Directions: Look at the three things that were said in the first part of the story. Draw a line from what was said to the name of character who said it.

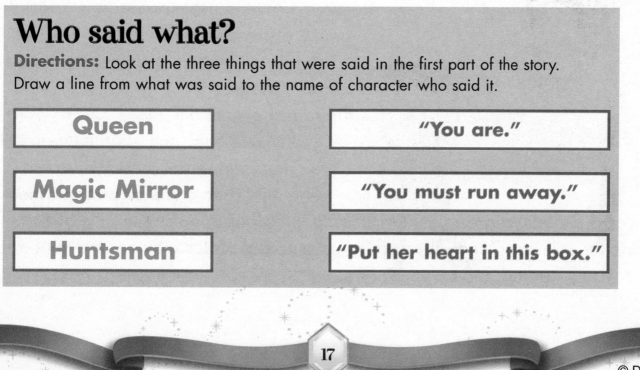

Queen	"You are."
Magic Mirror	"You must run away."
Huntsman	"Put her heart in this box."

Alone in the woods, Snow White was frightened. She started to cry. Birds and animals came out to see her. She felt better when she saw them.

"Is there a place where I could sleep?" she asked.

They led her to a little house in a clearing. There was no one home, but the sink was full of dirty dishes. There were seven little chairs and seven little beds. Snow White thought seven children lived in the house.

"Poor little things, they must not have a mother," she said.

Snow White liked to help. She swept and dusted, washed and scrubbed until everything was clean. Then she went upstairs and fell asleep.

When she woke up, a lot of little men were staring at her.

She told them dinner was almost ready. They would have to wash their hands before they ate. Every one of the Seven Dwarfs did. The soup smelled good, and they were very hungry. After they ate, they sang and danced. Then Snow White told a story. It was about the prince of her dreams.

In her room at the palace, the Queen asked, "Magic Mirror on the wall, who is the fairest one of all?"

The Mirror said Snow White was still alive. That made the Queen very angry.

She mixed up a pot of poison. She dipped a pretty red apple into it. She put the poisoned apple in a basket. Then the wicked Queen dressed up as an old peddler woman and set off for the woods to find Snow White.

What did you read?

Directions: Now that you have read the middle part of the story, answer the questions below.

1. After she was alone in the woods, who came out to see Snow White?

_____

2. When Snow White first saw the little house, who did she think lived there?

_____

3. After Snow White and the Dwarfs ate, what did they do?

_____

True or False?

Directions: Read each statement and circle the correct answer.

1. Snow White was happy to be alone.   True   False

2. The Dwarfs sink was full of dirty dishes.   True   False

3. Snow White told a story about cooking.   True   False

4. The Queen mixed up a pot of poison.   True   False

After the Seven Dwarfs went to work, the wicked Queen went to their house. Snow White was busy making pies. The wicked Queen pretended to be selling apples. She asked Snow White to taste one.

Snow White took just one bite of the apple and fell to the floor.

Snow White's animal friends had seen the old woman coming. They did not trust her. They went to get the Seven Dwarfs. The Dwarfs ran fast as they could. They got to the house just as the wicked Queen was leaving. They saw her running away.

The Dwarfs chased the Queen through the woods, and out onto a high, narrow ledge. Lightning hit the cliff. It broke the rock where the Queen was standing. Down she fell.

When the Dwarfs came back home, they found Snow White. She was still beautiful. She seemed to be asleep. They made a bed of gold for her. They put it in the woods.

Soon the Prince of a nearby kingdom heard about the girl in the forest. He came to see her for himself. When he did, he fell in love. She was the most beautiful girl he had seen in his life. He bent down and kissed Snow White, and the wicked Queen's spell was broken.

Snow White was very happy. She had dreamed this handsome prince would ride into her life. She knew the two of them would be together always. She thanked the Seven Dwarfs for their help. She kissed every one of them and waved good-bye.

What did you read?

Directions: Now that you have read the end of the story, answer the questions below.

1. After the Seven Dwarfs went to work, who went to their house?

_____

2. What did the wicked Queen pretend to be selling?

_____

3. The Dwarfs made a bed for Snow White. What was it made from?

_____

Who is Who?

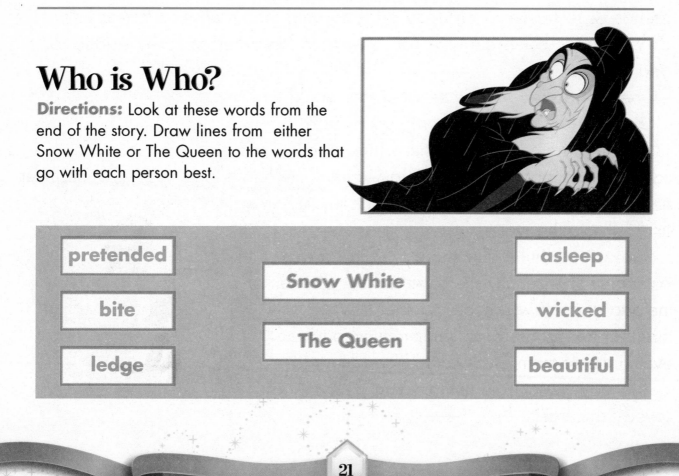

Directions: Look at these words from the end of the story. Draw lines from either Snow White or The Queen to the words that go with each person best.

pretended

bite

ledge

Snow White

The Queen

asleep

wicked

beautiful

The Little Mermaid

Once there was a Little Mermaid named Ariel. She was tired of living under the sea. Sometimes she swam up to the top of the water, even though her father did not like her to. Ariel wondered about the world above the sea.

"I love new things. I want to see more of them," Ariel said.

The land looked like a good place to be. Human beings lived there.

One day Ariel saw a new ship. She swam up to it as fast as she could. A young human was on the ship. Ariel thought he was handsome. Some of his friends were having a birthday party for him. The man was Prince Eric.

"We want to celebrate with you," his friends said. Then, they started to sing and dance.

One man asked the prince when he would marry.

"Oh, the right girl is out there somewhere, I just haven't found her, yet" the prince said.

Just then, a storm came up. Big waves tossed the ship from side to side. Prince Eric fell into the water.

Ariel pulled him to the shore. While he was asleep on the beach, she sang to him. She left before he could see her.

When her father, King Triton, found out what Ariel had done, he was very angry. He told her to stay away from human beings, but Ariel loved Prince Eric.

What did you read?

Directions: Now that you have read the first part of the story, answer the questions below.

1. What was Ariel tired of?

_____

2. What was the name of the man who Ariel saw on the ship?

_____

3. While the Prince was asleep on the beach, what did Ariel do?

_____

Recognize the Words

Directions: Look at these words in the list below. Put an **X** across any of the words that are **NOT** in the first page of the story.

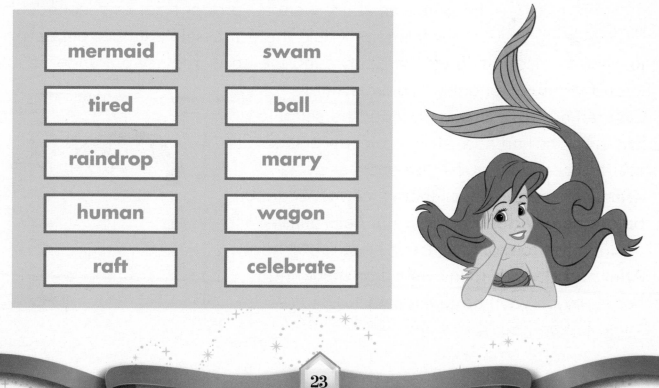

mermaid	swam
tired	ball
raindrop	marry
human	wagon
raft	celebrate

The evil sea witch, Ursula, was the only one who could help. Ariel went to see her.

"I know what you want," Ursula said. "I will make you human if you give me your voice."

Ariel thought about it.

"Oh, and one more thing," said Ursula. "If Prince Eric does not kiss you in three days, you are mine!"

"So, will you give me your voice?" Ursula asked.

"Yes, I will," Ariel said.

As soon as she spoke, Ariel had human legs. She could not swim. Her friends helped her to shore.

When Prince Eric found Ariel, he did not know who she was.

"Can you speak?" he asked.

She shook her head.

The next day, Prince Eric showed her around the kingdom. They went for a boat ride. Eric leaned over to kiss Ariel. The evil Ursula sent her pet eels out to the boat. The two eels swam around the boat. They swam under it. The eels were big and the boat was small.

On the third day, Ursula changed herself into a pretty girl. The girl had Ariel's voice in a shell. She wore the shell on a ribbon around her neck.

When Prince Eric heard that voice, he forgot all about the real Ariel. He could not help himself. He asked the girl to marry him.

Ariel's sea friends found out what Ursula had done. They all went up to the ship.

© Disney

What did you read?

Directions: Now that you have read the middle of the story, answer the questions below.

1. Ursula could give Ariel what she wanted. What did Ursula want from Ariel?

_____

2. When Prince Eric found Ariel, what did he ask her?

_____

3. On the third day, what did Ursula change herself into?

_____

4. Where did Ursula keep Ariel's voice?

_____

Match the people

Directions: Draw a line from the name of each character to the box that best describes who they are.

Ariel	I want Ariel's voice
Prince Eric	I took a boat ride with Prince Eric
Ursula	Showed Ariel the kingdom

There was a fight. The shell broke. Ariel could speak again. She told Prince Eric who she was. He did not have time to kiss her before the sun went down.

Ariel turned back into a mermaid. The evil Ursula took Ariel down into the sea. An old ship appeared in the battle that followed. Prince Eric jumped on the ship and fought Ursula. He saved Ariel. But Prince Eric could not stay in the sea with her. He had to breathe air to live.

Ariel was safe under the sea, but she was not happy. She and Prince Eric could never be together.

Her father, King Triton, loved Ariel very much. He did not want her to be sad. He made Ariel human again.

Prince Eric was very glad to see her. They were married right away.

What did you read?

Directions: Now that you have read the end of the story, answer the questions below.

1. After the shell broke, what was Ariel able to do?

_____

2. When the battle started, what appeared from the sea?

_____

3. King Triton did not want Ariel to be sad. What did he do for her?

_____

True or False?

Directions: Read each statement and circle the correct answer.

1. Ariel could speak again.   True   False

2. The shell would not break.   True   False

3. Triton loved Ariel very much.   True   False

4. Eric kissed her before the sun went down.   True   False

What did the stories say?

Directions: Answer the questions about some of the stories that you have read.

The Little Mermaid

1. Where did Ariel live?

   _____

2. What was the name of the Prince that Ariel fell in love with?

   _____

3. What did the evil sea witch, Ursula, want from Ariel?

   _____

Cinderella

1. Who lived with Cinderella and her Stepmother?

   _____

2. Who made it possible for Cinderella to go to the ball?

   _____

3. What time did Cinderella have to leave the ball?

   _____

4. What was Cinderella's fine coach made from?

   _____

Snow White and the Seven Dwarfs

1. Who did the Queen give a box to?

2. After Snow White washed and cleaned the little house, what did she do?

3. After the Seven Dwarfs went to work, what was Snow White busy doing?

4. After the Dwarfs made the bed of gold, where did they put it?

Beauty and the Beast

1. What did Belle's father take to the fair?

2. What was the name of the villager that wanted to marry Belle?

3. Name three of Belle's friends that lived in the castle?

4. Who did Belle and her father see on the balcony of the castle?

What did the stories say?

Directions: Answer the questions about some of the stories that you have read.

Sleeping Beauty

1. What were the names of the three good fairies?

   _____

   _____

2. The fairies said Aurora could live with them in the woods and be safe. She could return home after turning how old?

   _____

3. The fairies were late in trying to find Aurora. She had fallen into a deep sleep and only True Love's Kiss could awaken her. Then, the fairies cast a spell until they found Aurora's true love. What was the spell?

   _____

4. Flora, Fauna, and Merryweather hurried out to look for Prince Phillip. When they found him prisoner in Maleficent's castle and set him free, what two things did they give him?

   _____

   _____

ANSWER KEYS

PAGE 3

What did you read?

Directions: Now that you have read the first part of the story, answer the questions below.

1. What name did the king and queen give to their new child?

   Aurora

2. How many good fairies were invited to bless the child?

   three

3. Aurora would fall into a deep sleep only to be awakened by what?

   True Love's Kiss

4. Where did Aurora live with the fairies to be safe?

   the woods

Match the fairies
Directions: Each good fairy gave Aurora a gift. Draw a line from the name of each fairy to the gift she gave Aurora.

Fauna → The gift of beauty
Flora → to be awoken by True Love's Kiss
Merryweather → The gift of song

PAGE 5

Maleficent turned herself into a dragon and charged toward the prince. The dragon forced the prince out on the edge of a cliff. He had nowhere to go, but he could not fall. He had to save Aurora. He threw his enchanted sword into the dragon's heart. The dragon roared in pain.
Prince Phillip raced back to the castle and found Aurora. He bent down and kissed her. She woke up, and so did everyone else.
That night there was a ball. Aurora and the prince danced for a long time. The two fathers watched for a while. Then they started to plan a royal wedding.

What did you read?

Directions: Now that you have read the second part of the story, answer the questions below.

1. What was the birthday surprise that the fairies had for Aurora?

   It was time to live in the castle.

2. Why couldn't Aurora fall in love with the young man?

   She had to marry a prince.

3. When Aurora reached the tower room, what did she find?

   A spinning wheel.

4. What kind of creature did Maleficent turn herself into?

   A dragon.

PAGE 7

What did you read?

Directions: Now that you have read the first part of the story, answer the questions below.

1. Cinderella's stepmother was not kind. What two words describe her?

   Lazy and mean.

2. When Cinderella was sweeping, what did she hear?

   A knock at the door.

3. What did the messenger bring to her door?

   A big white envelope.

4. Whose gown did the birds and mice fix for Cinderella?

   Her mother's.

Kind words
Directions: Look at these words from the first part of the story. Circle only the words that describe Cinderella's stepmother or stepsisters.

kind | lazy
mean | pretty
lovely | angry

PAGE 9

The Prince did not know Cinderella's name. The slipper she had lost was his only clue. He promised to marry the girl whose foot fit the shoe.
When the Grand Duke came to the house, the stepsisters were excited. Each of them tried on the slipper, but it did not fit. It was too small.
The wicked Stepmother had locked Cinderella up in her room, but she got out. She came to the top of the stairs. She asked to try on the slipper.
"Yes, come down. Every maiden must try on the slipper," the Grand Duke said.
Cinderella slipped her foot into the glass slipper. It fit perfectly. She had always known it would.
The mean Stepmother and her daughters were very angry. Cinderella and the Grand Duke went to the palace together. The Prince was happy to see Cinderella again. Soon after, they were married.

What did you read?

Directions: Now that you have read the second part of the story, answer the questions below.

1. What did the Fairy Godmother turn the pumpkin and the mice into?

   A coach and four white horses.

2. What time did the Fairy Godmother say the spell would end?

   At midnight.

3. Who ran after Cinderella after she left? What did they find?

   The prince and Grand Duke. A slipper.

PAGE 11

What did you read?

Directions: Now that you have read the first part of the story, answer the questions below.

1. Name two things that Belle loved to do.

   Read and dream.

2. Where was Belle's father taking his new invention?

   At the fair.

3. Where did Belle find her father locked up?

   In the castle.

Belle and Papa
Directions: Look at these words from the first part of the story. Draw lines from either Belle or Papa to the words that go with each person best.

lost → Papa → inventor
reader → → old
dreamer → Belle → pretty

PAGE 13

What did you read?

Directions: Now that you have read the middle part of the story, answer the questions below.

1. After letting her father go, where did the Beast take Belle?

   To her room.

2. What did the teapot, clock and cup used to be?

   Servants at the castle.

3. Over time, Belle found that the Beast was not mean. What two words describe what Belle thought of him as they danced?

   Gentle and sweet.

True or False?
Directions: Read each statement and circle the correct answer.

1. The Beast found Papa in his castle. — True / **False**
2. The Beast used to be a servant. — True / **False**
3. Gaston asked Belle to marry him. — **True** / False
4. The villagers thought the Beast was kind. — True / **False**

PAGE 15

What did you read?

Directions: Now that you have read the end of the story, answer the questions below.

1. Who did Belle see on the balcony?

   Gaston and the Beast.

2. What was broken when Belle told the Beast she loved him?

   The spell.

3. When the spell was broken, what did the Beast turn into?

   A prince.

Belle or Beast
Directions: Look at these words in the list below. Put an X across any of the words that are NOT in the last part of the story.

roared | disliked ✗
slipped | handsome
happy | enchanted
loss ✗ | hurt
✗ | ✗

PAGE 17

What did you read?

Directions: Now that you have read the first part of the story, answer the questions below.

1. Who lived in the palace with Snow White?

   Her mean stepmother.

2. The Queen was proud to be beautiful. What did she stand in front of everyday?

   The Magic Mirror.

3. Where did the Queen want the Huntsman to take Snow White?

   Into the forest.

4. The Huntsman did not kill Snow White. What did he tell her to do?

   Run away.

Who said what?
Directions: Look at the three things that were said in the first part of the story. Draw a line from what was said to the name of character who said it.

Queen → "You are."
Magic Mirror → "You must run away."
Huntsman → "Put her heart in this box."

PAGE 19

What did you read?

Directions: Now that you have read the middle part of the story, answer the questions below.

1. After she was alone in the woods, who came out to see Snow White?

   Birds and animals.

2. When Snow White first saw the little house, who did she think lived there?

   Seven children.

3. After Snow White and the Dwarfs ate, what did they do?

   They sang and danced.

True or False?
Directions: Read each statement and circle the correct answer.

1. Snow White was happy to be alone. — True / **False**
2. The Dwarfs sink was full of dirty dishes. — **True** / False
3. Snow White told a story about cooking. — True / **False**
4. The Queen mixed up a pot of poison. — **True** / False

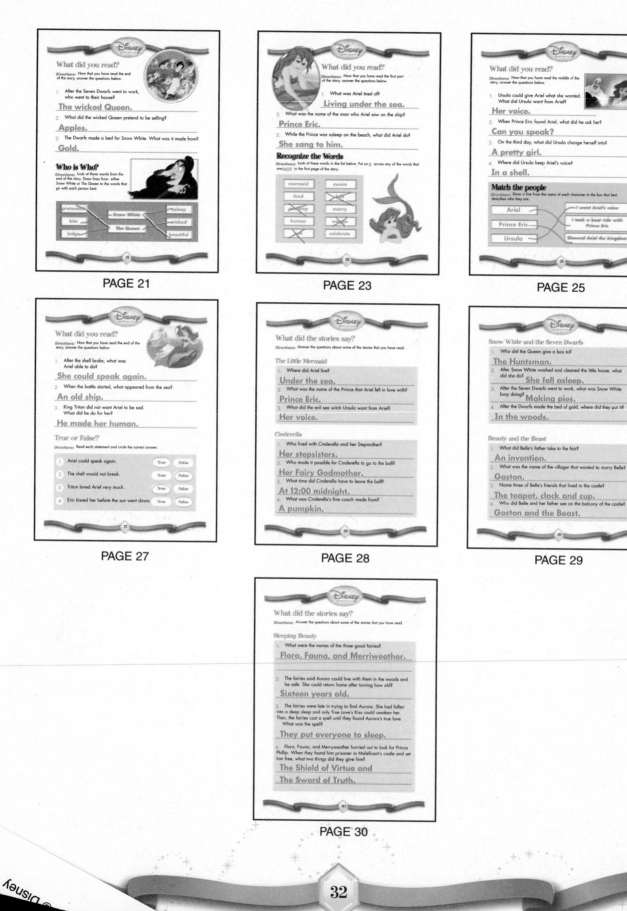

PAGE 21

PAGE 23

PAGE 25

PAGE 27

PAGE 28

PAGE 29

PAGE 30